JAZZ CLUB

club
piano
solos

VOLUME TWO

Stephen Duro *studied at the Royal College of Music under George Thalben-Ball (organ), Frank Merrick (piano) and Herbert Howells (composition).*

From the RCM, he won an organ scholarship to Pembroke College, Cambridge and then (after taking his degree) he went to Berklee School of Music in Boston on a special scholarship from 'Downbeat' magazine.

A Fellow of the Royal College of Organists, Stephen is much in demand as a teacher, performer and arranger. Among his recent successes have been an acclaimed series of master classes in Belgium and arrangements for the National Youth Jazz Orchestra.

His books include the successful I Can Play That!™ series of piano collections for Wise Publications.

Wise Publications
London/New York/Paris/Sydney/Copenhagen/Madrid

Exclusive Distributors:
Music Sales Limited
8/9 Frith Street,
London W1V 5TZ, England.
Music Sales Pty Limited
120 Rothschild Avenue,
Rosebery, NSW 2018,
Australia.

Order No. AM92014
ISBN 0-7119-4121-1
This book © Copyright 1995 by Wise Publications

Compiled by Peter Evans
Music arranged by Stephen Duro
Music processed by Allegro Reproductions
Book design by Pearce Marchbank, Studio Twenty
Quark'd by Ben May

Printed in the United Kingdom by
J.B. Offset Printers (Marks Tey) Limited, Marks Tey, Essex.

Your Guarantee of Quality
As publishers, we strive to produce every book to the highest
commercial standards.
The music has been freshly engraved and the book has been carefully
designed to minimise awkward page turns and to make playing from
it a real pleasure.
Particular care has been given to specifying acid-free,
neutral-sized paper made from pulps which have not been elemental
chlorine bleached. This pulp is from farmed sustainable forests and
was produced with special regard for the environment.
Throughout, the printing and binding have been planned to ensure
a sturdy, attractive publication which should give years of enjoyment.
If your copy fails to meet our high standards, please inform us
and we will gladly replace it.

early autumn

Words by Johnny Mercer
Music by Ralph Burns & Woody Herman

fever

Words & Music by John Davenport & Eddie Cooley

Moderate jump beat

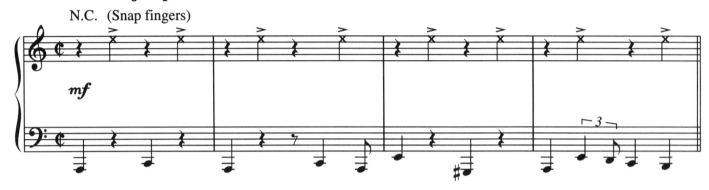

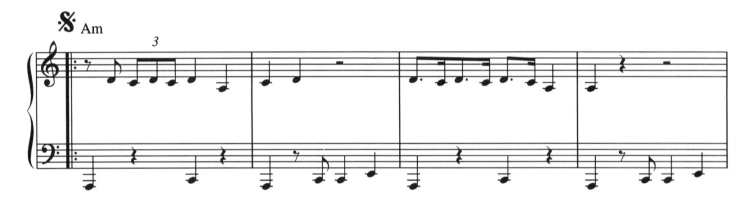

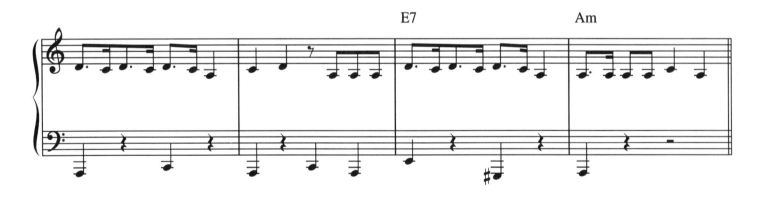

i'll be around

Words & Music by Alec Wilder

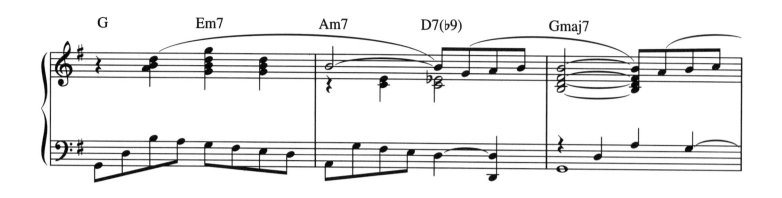

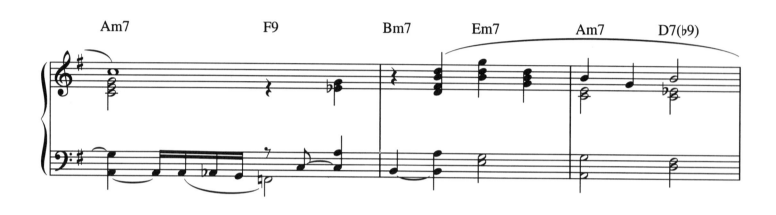

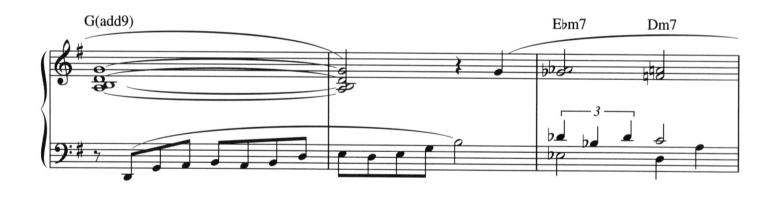

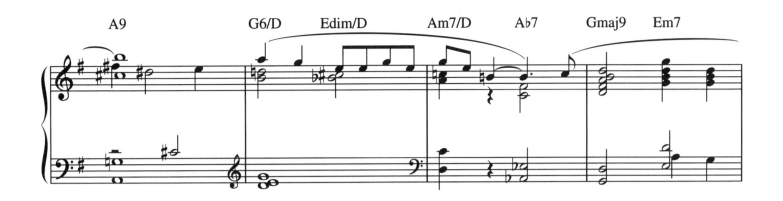

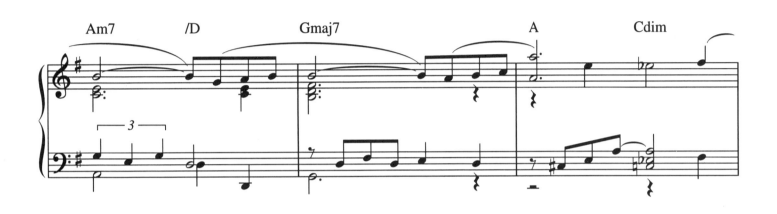

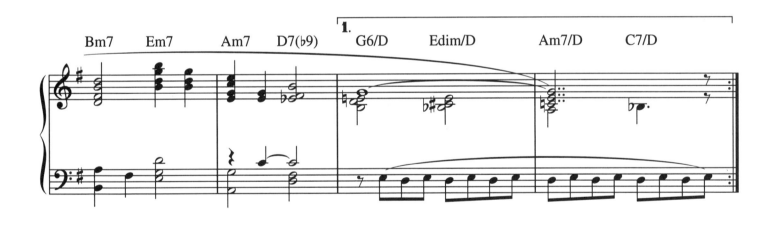

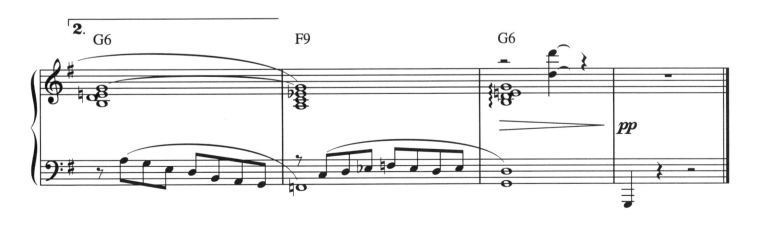

lazy river

Words & Music by Hoagy Carmichael & Sidney Arodin

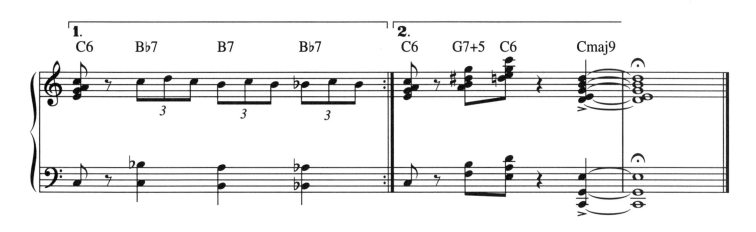

lush life

Words & Music by Billy Strayhorn

15

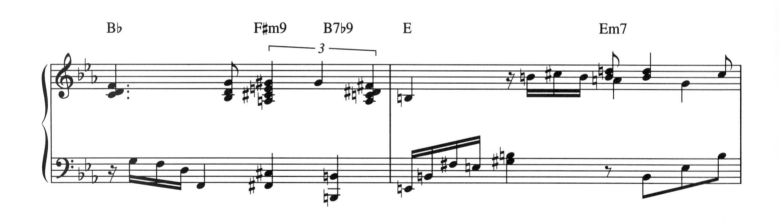

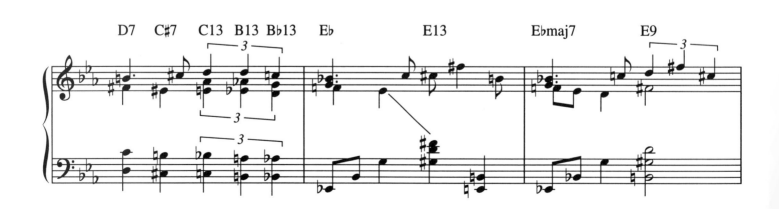

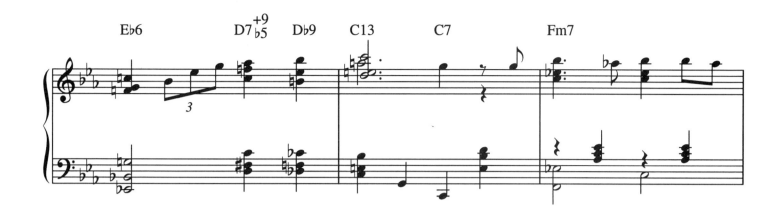

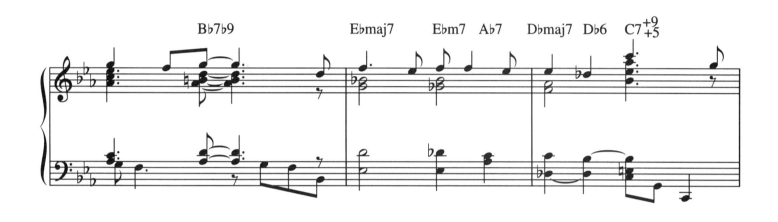

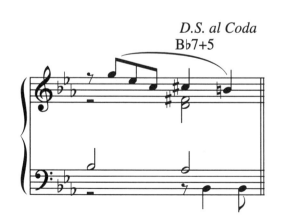

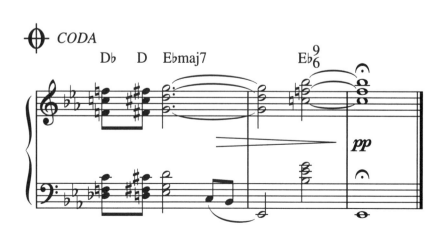

let's get away from it all

Music by Matt Dennis
Words by Tom Adair

Moderately

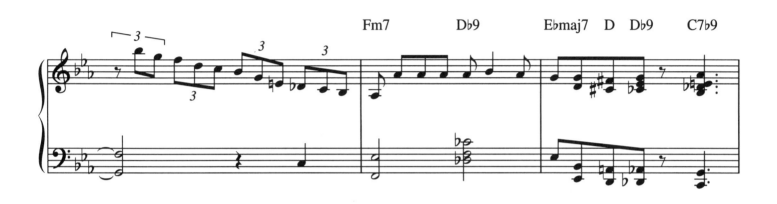

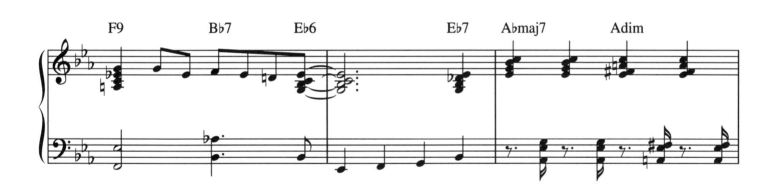

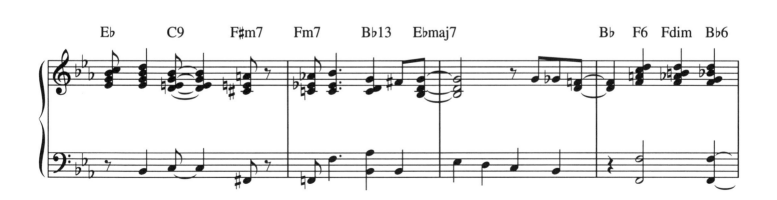

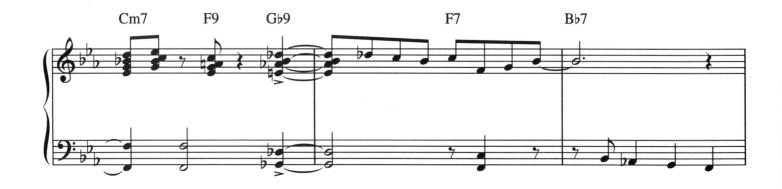

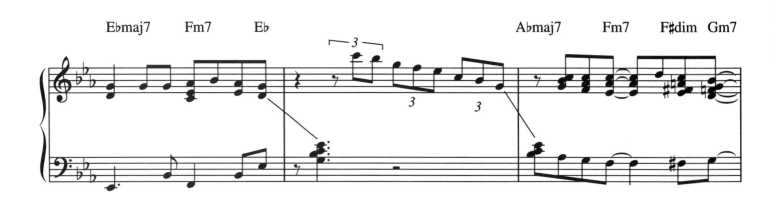

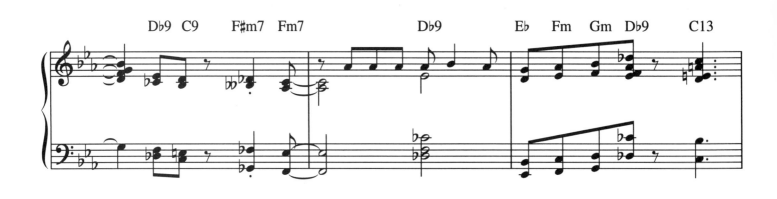

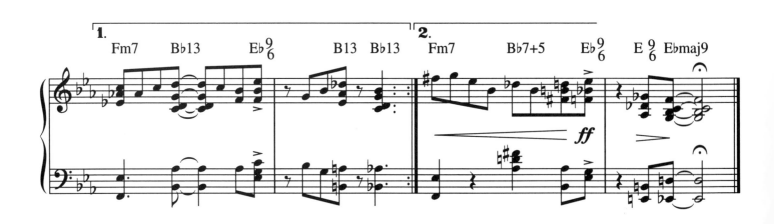

moanin'

Words by Jon Hendricks
Music by Bobby Timmons

Moderately

one note samba (samba de uma nota so)

Original Words by N. Mendonca
English Lyric by Jon Hendricks
Music by Antonio Carlos Jobim

To Coda ⊕

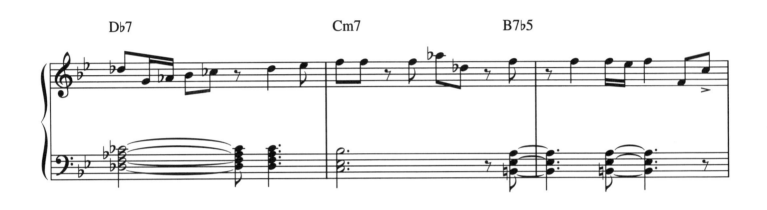

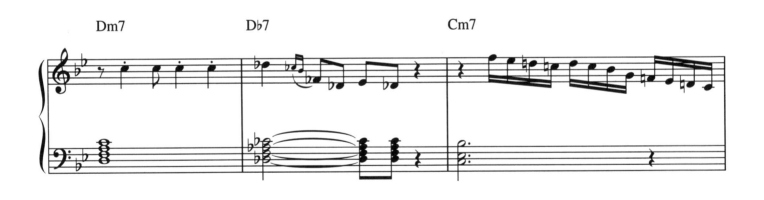

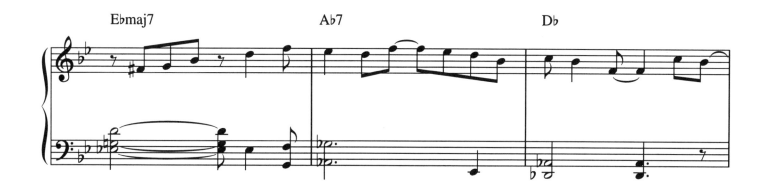

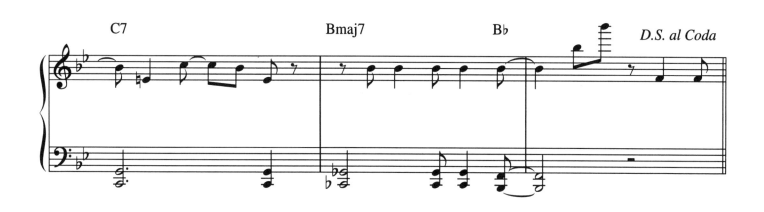

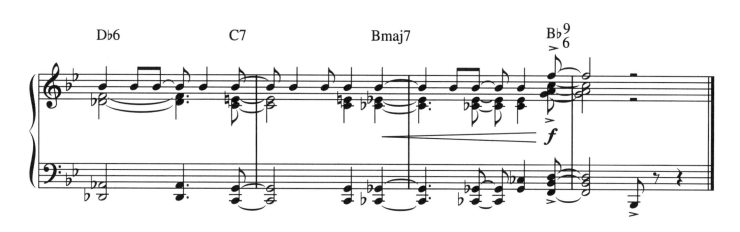

31

quiet nights of quiet stars (corcovado)

English Words by Gene Lees
Music & Original Words by Antonio Carlos Jobim

the midnight sun will never set

Words by Dorcas Cochran
Music by Quincy Jones & Henri Salvador

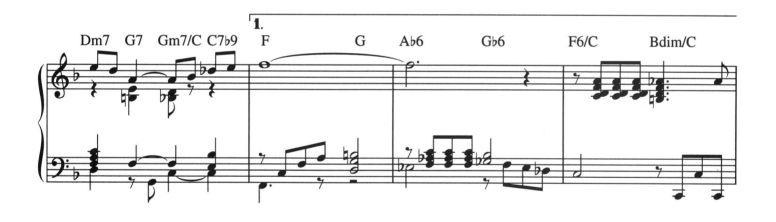

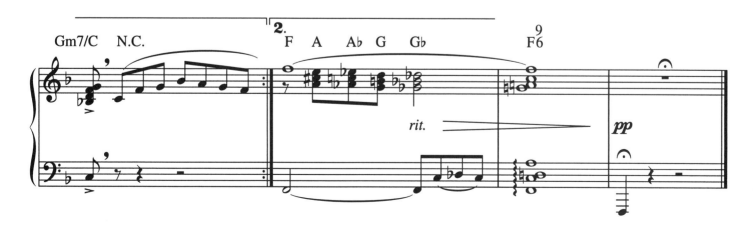

the late late show

Words & Music by Roy Alfred & Dave Cavanaugh

the preacher

By Horace Silver

walkin' shoes

By Gerry Mulligan

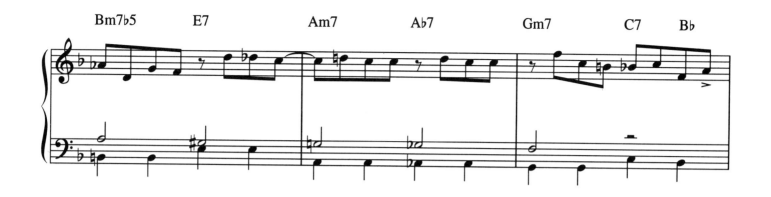

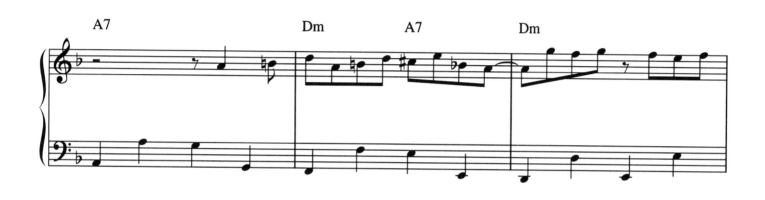

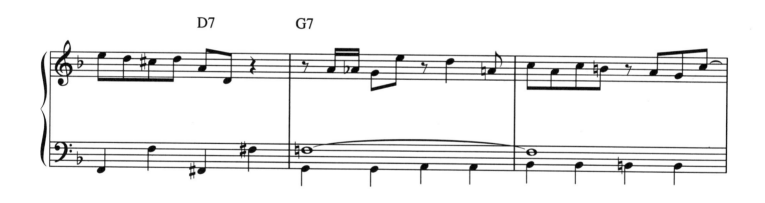

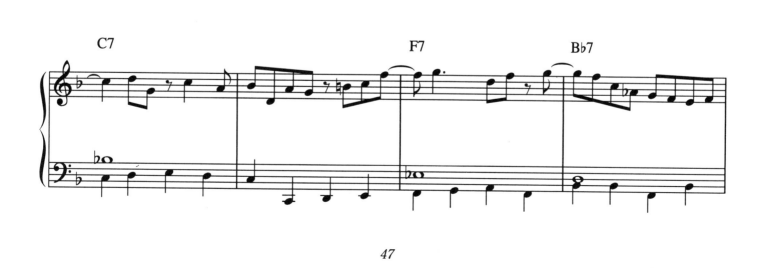

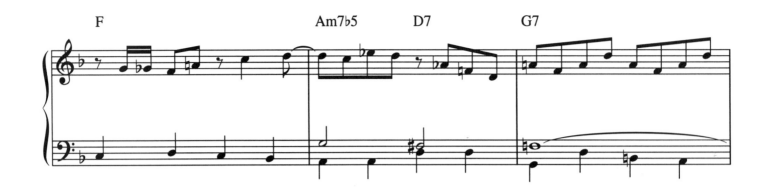

D.S. al Coda

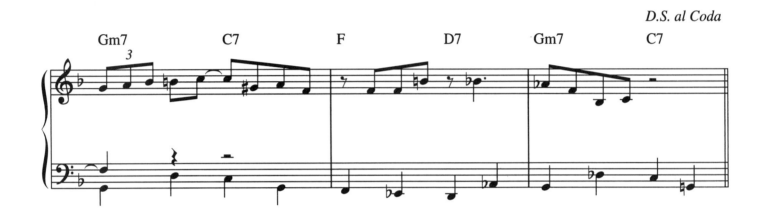